ARTHUR'S FIRE DRILL

朵拉的消防演习

（美）马克·布朗　绘著

范晓星　译

CHISO 新疆青少年出版社

When D.W. was a baby,
Arthur taught her
not to touch the hot stove.
"No!" he said. "Hot, hot!"

When D.W. was two years old,

Arthur taught her

about matches.

"No," he said.

"Never play with matches!"

Now D.W. is in nursery school.
Her teacher teaches her
all sorts of things…

How to tie her shoe,

how to print her name,

How to share.

1 One day the teacher said, "Listen up, boys and girls. Tomorrow we are going to have a fire drill."

6

She told them what to do.
"When the fire bell rings,
stop what you are doing
and quickly line up at the door."

Then she took them outside.

"Now stop, drop, and roll

 in the grass," she said.

They all stopped, dropped,

and rolled.

"This is fun!" said D.W.

"But what's it for?"

One of the Tibble twins said,

"It's if your clothes catch on fire."

"Oh!" said D.W. in a tiny voice.

That night D.W. whispered to Arthur,

"I'm not going to school tomorrow."

"Why not?" asked Arthur.

"There's going to be a fire," she said.

"You're making this up," said Arthur.

"Am NOT!" said D.W.

"Our teacher even

showed us what to do

when we catch fire tomorrow.

Stop! Drop! And roll!"

Arthur had to laugh.

"That's a fire DRILL,"

he said.

"It teaches you what to do
if there ever is a real fire."

"I don't care what you say," said D.W.

"I'm not going to school tomorrow."

"I have an idea," said Arthur,
and he went into his closet.
When he came out, he gave D.W.
his play firefighter's hat
and a very loud whistle.

"We'll have a fire drill at home,"
said Arthur,
"and you can be in charge."

"Great!" said D.W.
"I get to be the fire boss."
"But first," said Arthur,
"you need to know the rules."

Arthur's Fire Safety Rules

☑ Don't hide. Get outside!

Never go back in.

☑ Stay low and go!

If you have to go through smoke,

put a wet towel on your head

and crawl out.

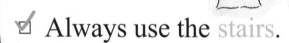

☑ Always use the stairs.

Never use the elevator.

☑ Be prepared!

Plan a way out now

with your family.

Always remember to first
get out of your house quickly.

Then go to a neighbor's house
to telephone the firehouse.

Just dial 911.

"Okay," said D.W. "I'm ready."

She ran down the stairs.

She blew her whistle. WHEEeee!

"Fire drill! Fire drill! Everyone out!

And don't forget Baby Kate,"

she shouted.

"WHAT!" said Dad.

"Just do what she says,"

said Arthur.

"She is the fire boss."

Pal ran out the door,

and the others quickly followed.

"What's all this about?"

asked Dad.

"It's D.W.'s homework,"

said Arthur.

"Tomorrow is her first fire drill."

D.W. had two more fire drills
that night.

"That's enough, D.W.," said Dad.

Then she made Arthur practice
how to get through fire or smoke.

"Hey! I'm all wet!"

shouted Arthur. "That's it!"

The next morning

D.W. was ready for school early.

But when she got there,

she saw a big red fire truck

out front.

"Oh, no!" she said.

"The school is on fire!

I need to get everyone out!"

Just then something strange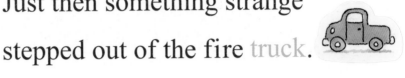
stepped out of the fire truck.
D.W. took one look at it
and screamed, "Help!
A monster!"

The strange thing said,

"Don't be afraid.

I'm not a monster.

I'm just a friendly firefighter."

And he took off his mask.

"See! This mask helps us

breathe in heavy smoke.

I'm here today to tell your class

how we fight fires.

Shall we go in?"

"I'll help, too,"

said D.W.

"I'm a fire boss."

After school,
Arthur asked D.W.,
"How was the fire drill?"
"No big deal,"
answered D.W.

24

译文

2. 朵拉还是小婴儿的时候，亚瑟就教她不要碰烤炉：

"别碰！烫！烫！"

3. 朵拉两岁的时候，亚瑟教她不要玩火柴：

"别碰，火柴可不能随便玩儿。"

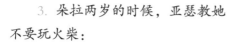

4. 现在，朵拉已经上幼儿园了。幼儿园的摩根老师教会她做很多事……怎样系鞋带，

5. 怎样写名字，

怎样和其他小朋友分享。

6. 有一天，摩根老师说："孩子们，都听好了，明天我们要举行一次消防演习。"

7. 摩根老师告诉小朋友们消防演习的时候应该怎么做："大家听到消防警报响起来的时候，就赶紧停下手里的事情，到门口排好队。"

8. 说完，摩根老师带孩子们来到教室外面，说："现在，请小朋友们在草地上练习'停，躺下，打滚'！"小朋友们全都听话地练习起"停"、"躺下"和"打滚"来。

9. "真好玩！"朵拉说，"可是我们这样做有什么用呢？"

丁丁和当当中的一个回答她："万一身上着火了，这样做可以灭火呀。"

"哦，明白了。"朵拉小声回答。

10. 晚上，朵拉悄悄对亚瑟说："我明天不想去上学了。"

"为什么？"亚瑟问。

"明天学校会着火的。"朵拉回答。

"你瞎编。"亚瑟说。

"我没有！"朵拉回答，"我们老师还教我们要是身上着火了该怎么办呢——'停，躺下，打滚'！"

"这是消防演习！"亚瑟笑了。

11. "消防演习是为了教会你们真正遇到着火时该怎么办。"亚瑟说。

"不管你怎么说，反正明天我就是不去上学。"朵拉回应。

12. "我有办法了。"亚瑟边说边走到衣橱前，取出一顶消防员的帽子和一个声音很响的哨子递给了朵拉。

28

13. "我们现在就来玩消防演习的游戏吧，"亚瑟说，"你来当指挥。"

"好呀！"朵拉说，"我要做消防演习总指挥。"

"没问题，不过首先，你得了解消防安全守则。"亚瑟回应。

14.

亚瑟的消防安全守则

☑ 不能藏起来，到室外去！别再回到室内。

☑ 走路的时候尽量贴近地面！如果必须穿过浓烟，请用湿毛巾包住脑袋，爬着穿过去。

☑ 发生火灾时，一定要走楼梯，不能坐电梯。

☑ 时刻准备好！事先和家人制定好火灾逃生方案。

15. 第一件事最最要紧，一定要先从房间里跑出来，然后到邻居家去给消防站打电话，拨119。

16. "我知道了，准备完毕！"朵拉说着就跑下楼去，吹响了口哨，呜！

"消防演习！消防演习！大家赶快出来！别忘了凯特宝宝！"她大声喊话。

17. "等一下！"爸爸回应。

"听朵拉的话！"亚瑟说，"她是消防演习总指挥。"

18. 小狗宝儿跑到门外，一家人也都跟了出来。

"你们这是要做什么？"爸爸问。

"我们在帮朵拉做家庭作业，"亚瑟回答，"明天是她第一次参加消防演习。"

19. 接下来，朵拉又指挥了两次消防演习。

"够了，朵拉。"爸爸说。

朵拉让亚瑟练习怎么穿过浓烟和火苗。

"嘿！我浑身都湿了！"亚瑟嚷嚷，"别闹了！"

20. 第二天，朵拉早早去上幼儿园。

走到幼儿园门口，她看见一辆红色大消防车停在那儿。

"哎呀，不好了！"她说，"幼儿园着火了！我得赶紧把大家都叫出来！"

21. 就在这时候，一个打扮得很奇怪的人从消防车里走下来。

朵拉一眼看见了，连忙大声喊："救命啊！有妖怪！"

22. 这个打扮得很奇怪的人说："别害怕，不是妖怪，我是超级好脾气的消防员叔叔。"说着，消防员叔叔摘下面罩，"瞧！这个面罩可以帮我们挡住浓烟。今天我来这里是想给你们讲讲应该怎样灭火，我可以进去吗？"

"我帮你，"朵拉回答，"我是消防演习总指挥。"

24. 放学回家，亚瑟问朵拉："消防演习怎么样？"

"小菜一碟！"朵拉回答。